CRACKS IN THE CLOISTER

CRACKS IN THE CLOISTER

By

BROTHER CHOLERIC

SHEED & WARD · NEW YORK
1954

CRACKS IN THE CLOISTER

Part I

NUTS IN THE NUNNERY

"Our postulant, Your Excellency...great on prayer."

"O. K.?"

"Repeat, Benedicamus Domino ...
and we've finished breakfast."

*"Sister, did you ever see a film
called 'Catherine the Great'?"*

*"But I never said I wanted
to be treated just the same
as everybody else."*

*"Well, as I always say, dear Mother,
if it's a sin it's a sin."*

*"And then for some reason
they didn't re-elect me . . ."*

*"In the world they used
to call me 'little funpot'."*

*"Speaking in Chapter
always gets me muddled."*

"Slipped disk, my foot."

"Same retreat giver as last year. What about it?"

"Oh but novenas make me much *worse."*

"That will do, Sister."

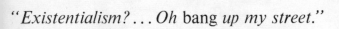

"Existentialism? ... Oh bang *up my street."*

"Any offers for an old scratch-dial?"

"Actually anything about Catholic Action
or the vernacular liturgy just gives me ulcers."

"Too Santa Clausy if you ask me."

"Happy feast."

*"Sweet of you to suggest it, Sister,
but I hate my favourite hymn-tune."*

"I said 'in virtue of Holy Obedience' . . . you heard."

"And you should see her genuflexions ..."

"Oh, so I can't even hear the Angelu any more, poor thing, can't I?"

"Sister, I like my novices to laugh at my jokes."

"'The echo of the angels' song', 'the Church's purest
hymn of praise'...trust you to muck it up."

"The chestnut is looking lovely, dear Mother . . .
    would you care for a little walk?"

"*But Sister, I don't a bit want to know what they
  do each year on Christmas Eve at your auntie's.*"

"*I was only saying to Sister that St. Romuald*
   was as deaf as a post and didn't give a curse."

"And now our little sister from the Missions
will show us how they do it in her community."

"You leave St. Thomas out of this."

"And as a special Christmas feature we're
having a polyphonic Asperges—*on ice."*

"Sad rather."

"And when he's got to '...in excelsis DEo',
Sister, in *you come with the wind."*

"God's lovely fresh air."

Part II

MUFFINS WITH THE MONKS

*"Here's another very beautiful little
motet. Actually it is a samba."*

"Who's pinched my relic of the Little Flower?"

"Another server for Father."

"One must remember, Brother, that psychiatry
is still virtually in its infancy."

"Well, Abbess, and how's the old blood-pressure?"

*"Oh, just another of these screamingly
funny Latin jokes, that's all."*

"And it doesn't go back till they make me Abbot."

"Behold, you are the crown of Israel and the lily of Juda . . . you are the rippling brook of Ephraim and the sweet-smelling bough of Benjamin."

"No, not straight in; I believe he had
        some job or other in the world."

"Rather ham, don't you think?"

"Heard the news?—no pontifical."

"All right then, you put 'bingo' into Latin."

"Liturgy? Gosh, yes."

The breviary with its direct and simple worship...

"Once through the Creed again, please, and then
you shall have your Teddy Bears' Picnic.*"*

"*Accidie? Accidie?...never heard of it.*"*

*Whenever accidie begins to overcome a monk, it either
makes him stay in his cell idle and lazy, or it drives
him out from thence and makes him restless and unable
to settle to any kind of work.

(*Cassian, Institutes*)

*"Well, about half way through Vespers
I felt something in my psyche go* ping."

"Me sit down to eat porridge? When I was
a novice, we used to sleep *standing up."*

"Great admirer of a man called Dior."

"He says penicillin's sissy."

*"Steady on, Brother, you're not a cover
design for* In a Monastery Garden, *you know."*

"Tomorrow I'll do cantor."

"Say what you like, there's nothing in the Rule against it."

"And that funny noise you hear is Vespers."

"You and your Jerusalem gaude . . ."

"Cod—on St. Benedict's Day."